FARMING IN THE

A Portrait in Old Photographs and Prints

ANTHONY DAY

S. B. Publications

By the same author:
Turf Village (1983)
Wicken: A Fen Village in Old Paintings (1990)
Fen and Marshland Villlages (1993)
But For Such Men as These (1994)

For my father who gave his life to farming for so little reward

First published in 1995 by S.B. Publications
c/o 19 Grove Road, Seaford, East Sussex BN25 1TP

ISBN 1 85770 083 X

Typeset, printed and bound by MFP Design and Print, Longford Trading Estate, Thomas Street, Stretford, Manchester M32 0JT.

CONTENTS

Front cover: The horse-drawn drill was an anachronism when this photograph was taken c.1965 — and that is why it was taken. It was no showpiece for onlookers, but was genuinely at work, a Smythe drill set for four rows of sugar beet, on the Cole Ambrose estate at Stuntney near Ely. This farmer kept faith with horse-power longer than any other in the region, but the changeover had to come — and very soon after this photograph was taken, inevitably reducing the workforce. Renowned for his upkeep of horses, carts and implements, Cola Ambrose certainly did attract onlookers from the road, gazing in acute nostalgia. The man in charge of the horses here is Harris Venney, who was the Ambrose horsekeeper for many years. His son and daughter still work on the estate. The man behind the drill is 'Ganger' Payton. A bypass slices across the landscape today where Ely Cathedral lends majesty like no other edifice in the fenland.

(Cambridgeshire Collection)

INTRODUCTION

It was once a dense forest region, swept down by the interglacials of the ice age that left Britain an island. All the trees fell in the same direction and they can be found today. Carvings and walking sticks are still made from them. Tree-covered islands were left standing and silt islands rose, but the rest was a swamp covering some 1,300 square miles between Cambridge, Lincoln and The Wash. Very slowly this region was to evolve into England's broadest plain, its wheatbelt and market garden.

An extension of the sea in winter, it was in summer partly dry with rich pastures and some soil for the using. The first settlers here were short, dark-haired neolithic Iberians and they gave way to Aryan Celts, the Goidels and Britons from Northern France who were the red-haired tribes that repelled the Roman hordes of Julius Ceasar in 55BC. When the Romans tried again, successfully, in AD44 they had to repel the Girvii of the fens and Boudicca's Iceni of Norfolk.

The Romans faced up to the problems of the fens. From their causeways they saw the possibility of growing food there and created drainage schemes. They raised a barrier against The Wash to create the silted area we call Marshland, but it proved hard work for little reward on land below sea level. The Saxons that followed became the chroniclers of the fens but allowed them to revert to their old state, populated by this time by wild men, including dispossessed Britons, facing incursions from the Vikings.

Thereafter the history of the fens is a long sequence of attempts to lose the waters while the inhabitants rejoiced in the lack of success, becoming a race apart, protective of their way of life, despising the 'Uplanders', as they called them. Ugly by all accounts, web-footed even, these men had come to rely on the meres for fish and wildfowl while nurturing livestock on the high ground and summer pastures.

They lived above the waters in dwellings like huge beehives made of wattle and daub and reeds, with interiors softened by fleeces, hides and feathers; they took to the waters in coracles made of osiers and skins, and they learned, where trees could not thrive, to dig out the rotted vegetation and to dry it for fuel.

When later embankments gave way and drowned out the inhabitants of Marshland in 1607, King James I acted to help the survivors, but the scheme he advocated for draining six hundred acres at Waldersea between March and Wisbech was unsuccessful in the undertaking and it was in the reign of his successor, the doomed Charles I, that real action was taken, once and for all, to reclaim the fen country. The Duke of Bedford gathered about him his Company of Adventurers to undertake a drainage scheme led by the experienced Dutch engineer, Cornelius Vermuyden, their reward being the acquisition of drained land.

Vermuyden used the old rivers — most, if not all, cut by the Romans — but cut new channels with sluices to control the outlet to the sea and this scheme put despair and anger into the hearts of the fenmen who rebelled, attacking the diggers and dykes and taking lives. The drainers won and those untamed fenmen slowly transformed into farmers on the low levels as well as the high.

The winning of this fertile plain where the soil is vegetable and not mineral, divided into the South, Middle and North Bedford Levels, brought other problems. The dried-out peat began to erode at the rate of two inches a year and it has never stopped. The land gradually sank below the river levels until horse-powered pumps had to be installed to lift the water. Windmills followed which had to be replaced as the level sank and the more permanent structures built for steam from 1820 were facing an acute problem a hundred years on when their scoopwheels could be lowered no further. Diesel took over just in time and then the electricity that governs drainage today.

Another hazard soon hitting the farmers were the dust storms, or 'blows rising when the peat was at its driest and finest in spring and autumn, taking the crops with them, a phenomenon made worse in our time by the felling of trees and uprooting of hedges to make way for modern machinery. It was soon discovered too that any bonfire on fen land can set fire to the peat. And, inevitably, nature did its best at times to restore the fens to their old state, bursting the banks when the high tides prevented the outlet to the sea.

It became a matter of discovering what grew best on the fens and the produce from them has continued to change with new needs and tastes. Farming there has always been hazardous. The many smallholders living in isolation knew all about poverty and deprivation, as did their children and workers if they had any. Floods might return at any time to spoil their crops and even today when the land is well drained the water can lie on the surface long enough to cause permanent damage. The compensation is that when crops thrive they are heavy.

The second world war eased the lot of these farmers with its guarantees and the laying of hard surfaces over some of the peat tracks to carry ever more sophisticated machinery. Illustrating aspects of farming in the fens in this book leads me to wonder what they will look like and what purpose they will serve in a hundred years' time, for the peat is disappearing fast and the huge tonnages of sugar beet, potatoes, carrots, onions and salad crops will eventually have to come from somewhere else. The fens have gone full circle in that irrigation is seen to be the first necessity for many crops, the river water being returned from whence it came, flushing down the surface faster. If this is farming as if there will be no tomorrow, than it has its logic.

HARVESTING THE REEDS

Those early fenmen took from the fen only what nature provided — plentifully. To this day reeds are harvested in the Norfolk Broads and Wicken Fen for use in thatching. They once provided secure insulation inside dwellings, even into this century, lining walls and ceilings, and in a few cottages they are still there. For reeds are firm and long-lasting, overlooking their combustibility. Here the painter Robert Macbeth R.A. depicts reed-cutting in Wicken Fen in 1878, adding Victorian charm to the hard labour. Macbeth took to the fens through his friend Robert Farren, the Cambridge artist, and liked Wicken in particular where the character of the landscape had remained unchanged for centuries. Today the reeds are cut in winter in North Adventurers' Fen, which is adjacent to Wicken Fen, and if they grow taller and thinner than before it is probably due to the fertilizers feeding into the water from the surrounding land under cultivation. A further tract of this has, however, recently been taken over by the National Trust.

(Author's Collection)

HARVESTING THE SEDGE

The grass-like sedge that grows where it is wet in winter and dry in summer was, and still is, harvested for thatch and its capping, and was much used as a litter. The full name of Wicken Sedge Fen tells all. The whole area was once dug for turf but its later use, when divided into small private plots, was for harvesting sedge, for which there was a constant demand. It so happened that this intervention in a primeval landscape encouraged insects that attracted the men of science and thus led to its being acquired by the National Trust. The sedge was cut every two or three years which ensured strong, lasting quality. These laden sedge boats early this century are on Burwell Lode, conveying the produce of Wicken Fen to the next village. South Adventurers' Fen, which is part of Swaffham Fen, lies opposite.

(Cambridgeshire Collection)

THE WILDFOWLERS

Fen Slodgers, they called them — a word you will not find in the OED — revealing one way of catching wildfowl c.1750. Guns were invented by this time but silent means were best, including the use of the duck decoy where a long cage with a wide opening tapered to a point where the ducks, lured there by a dog running alongside, could be taken. Netting was another means of capture. A small island about thirty-four inches long and a mere four inches wide was made, and a net with a mesh designed to catch a particular bird of that habitat was spread over it and stained the colour of the ground. A tethered decoy bird or a whistle imitating the cry of that bird was used to attract the prey. Held to the ground on one side, the net could be pulled over the settling birds by the hidden wildflower using a string attached to pulleys. He would have taken account of the habits of birds flying with the wind, as in the case of lapwings, or against the wind as with ruffs and reeves. The town markets were waiting for all they could catch.

(Cambridgeshire Collection)

THE PUNT GUNNER

Meres deep and shallow remained all the year round after the fen drainage was under control and these were the haunts of the last remaining fenmen devoted to living off the wild. Then there were the washes, designed to take the overflow from the rivers during the wet season, spreading as of old like the sea and attracting waterfowl in great numbers. The washes between the Old and New Bedford Rivers, stretching from Earith to Denver for twenty-two miles, are more than half-a-mile wide in places and the stretch at Welney is maintained as a sanctuary for waterfowl. This punt gunner, Charlie Scholes, is seen on Cowbit Wash by the river Welland near Spalding in the 1890s, and he is not there in the service of sport but to make a living. He is on ice in this case, having adapted a sledge for the purpose of using his muzzle-loading gun to shoot the wild geese.

(Cambridgeshire Collection)

THE FISHING FAMILIES

This old couple, seen near Ely in the 1880s, are leftovers
from a wilder time, still dedicated to taking what the
rivers offer free, relying on well-maintained nets and eel
grigs to make their living, and finding plenty of demand
for what they catch. Catching fish individually by rod
and line or by using darts or eel glaives was never for
them and there many such families remaining in the fens
long after drainage had made it an agricultural region.
Today there are more fishermen than ever before but
using rod and line only in the fen rivers, fishing more
often than not in competition and seldom keeping their
catch. This couple would have scoffed at that.

(Cambridgeshire Collection)

THE EEL TRAPPER

Fenmen were for long dependent on fish and eels were in huge supply and demand. They came into the Domesday Book valuations and the entry for Wicken reads: 'The Earl himself holds Wicham. TRE it answered for seven hides. Land to twelve ploughs. In the demesne are three hides and three ploughs; and a fourth can be made. Eleven villages and eight boarders have there eight ploughs. There are five bondmen; and three mills of twenty-eight shillings, and four-thousand and two-hundred and fifty eels; meadow for twelve ploughs; pasture for the cattle of the village and by custom three nets in the mere of Saham. For all dues it is and was worth fourteen pounds; TRE six pounds. Fair Eddeva held this manor.' The survey was simply to estimate taxable property, and eels were that important then. Soham Mere is dry today but there are eels aplenty in the rivers and the lakes left by excavation. Most are caught by rod and line, but eel grigs such as that on the left of this picture and the smaller eel traps like that being made here by Paul Gotobed (a very old fen name) behind his premises near Lisle Lane, Ely, are still used by a few, along with eel nets, to supply London markets. The traps are baited and sunk, and the larger eels that enter cannot exit until they are poured into boats. Mr Gotobed, seen early this century, lived in the place named after the fish.

(Cambridgeshire Collection)

THE PIKE

They are bigger than this only when they get away! If the pike is the traditional scavenger of the fen waters, it was, and is, welcome for its size and, today, the sport it affords. This old fen fisherman of 1897 shows his pleasure in his catch — as far as he can without spoiling the shot. This huge pike would have to be cut up and spread around before it deteriorated, but the man holding it would be contemplating the prospect of fish within the fish, quite big enough to eat. If it is the biggest he has handled, he might be thinking of having it stuffed to show it off for the rest of his life, a common enough practice then. Otherwise, what would he have given for a freezer? Pike is served today in traditional fen restaurants, such as The Old Fire Engine House, Ely.

(Cambridgeshire Collection)

PRODUCE OF THE FEN

Reeds, sedge and peat turves for burning formed the produce of Wicken Fen for centuries and the scene here summarising this is at the mouth of Wicken Lode, an ancient channel used for transporting all three commodities into our time. The turf shed on the left belonged to turf merchant and shopkeeper Bill Norman who paid the parish council a mooring fee of two shillings and sixpence a year, as did another merchant, Mark Bailey, while the third at this time, Josiah Owers, paid five shillings for having his shed nearer the village. We have here a turf-vendor's cart with donkey, a turf barrow, a tumbrel loaded with sedge off Poors' Fen behind, a stack of turves and some bundled reeds beyond. Men who never sowed their crops existed off this fen for a very long time.

(Author's Collection)

THE TURF INDUSTRY

The Roman probably dug it, but the burning of dried peat for domestic fuel goes back a very long way. There was nought else to burn where trees were so scarce apart from dried cattle-dung, and there was not enough of this to last out the winters. Yet the use of this may well have encouraged the digging out of rotted vegetation and drying it for fuel, and, once the right quality was ascertained that ensured slow combustibility, the fen winters grew much warmer. The peat lay very deep in some areas, trapped between layers of clay and betraying periods of formation. Only the top layer was useful for fuel, and from the right depth it dried into solid blocks that could be used for insulation as well as fuel. They were neat workers, those turf diggers. After clearing of some fifteen inches of surface, they cut a trench one-spit deep and four across, using a becket, a thin spade with a right-angled flange to shape a neat brick. The digger worked swiftly and rhythmically, pushing the becket into the soaked peat without the aid of a foot, and building a precise wall beside his trench. It was hard but not heavy work, done between March and August, and he could dig as many as three-thousand turves a day for his piecework wages which included contingent jobs. This man is digging in Burwell Fen in the 1920s here the surface was lowered considerably by the industry that ended in 1939

(Cambridgeshire Collection)

MARKETING THE TURVES

Here the turf-digger is dressing — or opening — his wall of turves to aid their drying within the usual time of six weeks, depending on the weather. They were then taken by turf barrow — sometimes precariously over narrow planks across dykes or drains — to the stacks by the lodes for transportation by boat to the turf sheds or straight on to barges for transportation to the towns, although turves stood a long time before being considered fit to burn. These stacks in Burwell Fen in the 1920s were clearly accessible to pony and cart. Dressing was done at great speed. Before the becket was introduced in Isleham Fen in the 1850s, the digging tool was the moor spade or sharp shovel with its heart-shaped blade. Turf was sold by measure to prevent the adding of water to dry turves to fool the buyers, and the measure was divisions of a hundred. The Isleham becket was small, but when the larger Wicken becket was introduced the merchants reduced their hundred to sixty while still calling it a hundred, and the custom remained, puzzling a few first-time buyers. Bert Bailey of Wicken was the last professional turf digger who set aside his becket in 1939, closing an industry that had employed thousands of people throughout the fens.

(Cambridgeshire Collection)

OSIERS

Willows grow as naturally as reeds on the wetlands, and it was not long before a widespread use was made of them. They were soon contributing to an industry, leading to the planting of osier beds such as we see here late last century, showing how the young willows are trimmed down to sprout again the next year, ensuring the slim stems needed for basket making. After drainage the willows were planted in the wet areas, often on the washes by the rivers, and they provided work on the fen level for many men, women and children for one month of the year, which was the time devoted to the cutting. One sharp hedgehook, constantly whetted by a stone rub, was the only tool needed for the harvesting, and the same willows would serve for many years.

(Cambridgeshire Collection)

WOMEN AMONG THE OSIERS

The impression that these women are making a clumsier job of cutting osiers is false. They are simply at work in an overgrown plantation, preparing for a straighter crop next year, and what they are cutting would be of no use to the basketmakers. Cutting was generally a man's job, while the women and children would be employed in the stripping, doing one of the temporary casual jobs set aside for them throughout the year. At other times the women would be potato planting and picking, or onion or fruit picking, leaving off soon enough to get home to cook for their hungry husbands and children. Here, late last century, they look cool and well-laundered, but then they are composing themselves for the camera.

(Cambridgeshire Collection)

AN OSIER FAMILY

The camera lies in so far as these osier strippers are not dressed for the work in hand as much as a Sunday gathering. The scene is Sutton-in-the-Isle late last century. The osier stems, having been soaked, were pulled through the iron glave like that held by Mr Butler Frear on the extreme left. Such glaves were made by the local blacksmiths who took pride in a degree of ornateness. The Frear family is prominent here. The back row, left to right, are: Mrs Liz Darby, Miss Gage, Mrs Tom Read, unidentified, Mrs Minnie Darby, Mrs Isaac Fulcher, Mrs Sarah Frear and the boy Charlie Frear. Middle: Mrs Tom Stimpson and her daughter, Mrs George Stimpson, Mrs Nelly Youngs. Front: Ethel Joyce with Florence Frear, Mrs Fanny Frear holding her baby and Miss Stimpson with two unidentified children, as is the boy behind, right. The barn behind survived until May 1980. Basketmakers often had their own osier beds. The name Frear occurs in Sutton today but there are more of them in St Ives not far away.

(Cambridgeshire Collection)

COPROLITE

There was more of value below the surface of the fens than men realised before the nineteenth century. It was enough to take out the peat, the underlying clay for bricks and the gravel, marl, clunch and lime from the higher ground, until a discovery was made in 1858. John Ball of Burwell, who was already well known for turning bones and dried blood into fertilizer, took samples of prehistoric animal and shellfish residue from near the surface, washed away the clay, ground nodules into a powder in his mill, and treated them with an acid to compound a proven fertilizer. Thus began an industry that turned into the fen goldrush, bringing in workers to swell the village populations, all aiming to cash in while supplies and demand lasted. A plant was installed by Burwell Lode to process coprolite, a name derived from a Greek word meaning dung stone, and this plant later evolved into a general fertilizer factory taken on by Fison, Packard and Prentice. As this picture shows, the excavation was deep, but the land had to be restored behind them for agriculture. Then, obviously, the product was returned to the land in modified form. The industry gradually declined to the end of the century, killed off not only by diminishing supplies in some areas, but by imports after coprolite had been uncovered abroad. Ribbed patterns on bare fields can still be seen from the air, betraying the former activity of coprolite mining.

(Cambridgeshire Collection)

TRANSPORTING THE COPROLITE

While farmers were paying their men ten shillings a week, the coprolite industry was offering between two and three pounds, so the farmers were compromised by loss of labour. Thus compensation for the loss of their land to excavation was very welcome. Digging out the coprolite, however, was never an easy job, and the money was hard-earned. No fewer than seventy-three of Cambridgeshire's one-hundred and forty-five villages show a big rise in population at the height of the industry in the early 1870s, and a rather sudden fall as it declined. No expense was spared to transport the coprolite. Three-and-a-half miles of railway were laid to serve the Burwell factory and a chain ferry was installed on the lode. Some of the engaged workers went on to work in the fertilizer and cement factories that took over the coprolite factory sites. The biggest of these remains at Barrington, Cambridgeshire. Temporary rails could be laid to get the coprolite from the workings to the factories, as we see here, affording the men a quiet, if smoky, ride before the unloading. It was an industry that needed the machine age to thrive.

(Cambridgeshire Collection)

WOAD

The Roman invaders gazed more in astonishment than fear at the ancient Britons with blue skins, dyed that colour in the belief it would scare their enemies. Any other colour would have served as well, but the plant woad produced a blue dye and that had to serve. Isatis Tinctoria, the woad plant, is a biennial herb sprouting leaves in its first year and flowers and seeds in its second year. Its roots penetrate down to about eighteen inches, and it grew straight up to a height of between two and five feet with the flowers forming at the top, and it was grown widely in England, including the fens, for that dye used for clothes, once primitive skin dyeing had gone out of fashion. In the middle ages the colour green was obtained by mixing woad blue with yellow weld from another plant. Madder from a third plant mixed with woad made purple, and such vegetable dyes were used for a very long time. They engendered a big industry in colourful Elizabethan times, and woad was grown plentifully in North Lincolnshire. It was grown too in Long Sutton, Moulton Common, Tydd St Mary and Parson Drove, where the last woad mill in this region was demolished in 1914. These are woad stooks where the crop has been left for seed, with the Parson Drove mill in the background, early this century.

(Cambridgeshire Collection)

CULTIVATING WOAD

The woad seeds were broadcast two-to-three bushels to the acre until drills were introduced, which cut the amount to less than half. It was sown in April and May in rows ten-inches apart. Weeding was essential, and this was a job often given to children of the poor who were beyond complaining. Drills made this weeding easier using short spuds and hoes, wearing padding about the knees when crawling as was done later when singling sugar beet or mangolds. When the woad had grown to about ten inches it was cropped to about three inches off the ground, which caused it to branch out for easier gathering of the leaves for the dye. Once it had sprouted again, a second gathering would be made. The gathered woad leaves were tipped into a heap about twenty-feet long and three-feet wide, then carted to the crushing mill, seen here, where they were crushed by giant roller, pulled round a circular platform by a horse attached to a pole. The horse had its own track round the platform and the pole prevented it from stepping on to the platform. No horse could enjoy this job, but each was limited to an hourly shift from a team of horses on hand.

(Cambridgeshire Collection)

CRUSHING THE WOAD

Three rollers were generally used to crush the woad, but some mills had as many as eight rollers, each weighing more than a ton, measuring seven-and-a-half-feet in diameter at the wide end and six feet at the other, with poles to keep the rollers apart. In some mills, engines took over the job of turning them. Horses had been used for such treadmill jobs for a very long time, but none was more exhausting than this. Turning butter churns and hay elevators was nothing by comparison, the monotony meaning little to them after a while.

(Cambridgeshire Collection)

PROCESSING THE WOAD

After the crushing the woad was balled, dried, crushed again, couched, casked and at last conveying to the dye factories, firstly by horsepower, then by railway. Here the two men are kneading the woad leaves into dense balls, continuing the process of refining down. Two other woad mills survived this one at Parson Drove. That at Algarkirck came down in 1927, and that at Skirbeck in 1932, after processing the crop of that year. As a dye, woad was overtaken by indigo from India.

(Cambridgeshire Collection)

THE PLOUGHMEN BEGIN

Among the earliest crops planted into the drained fens were turnips and onions, but farming there was tentative for a long time. With courage mounting, there was a setback to the ideal when the original Denver sluice collapsed in 1713, leaving a vast area to revert to wild fen for thirty-five years while drainers and navigators argued for and against rebuilding. Meanwhile, hunting for survival resumed until the new sluice was built and farming could resume. The drainage was far from perfect for its healthy continuation, but when the peat was dry, it was soft and malleable, as this poor-man's method of ploughing it, as depicted by Robert Farren in the 1880s, shows. There was, however, still widespread reliance on fish and wildfowl for food, while attempting to beat the hazards of farming in the fens.

(Cambridgeshire Collection)

OXPOWER

They were lighter of foot than horses, and just as easily trained to subject themselves to the service of man. Oxen were still being used on a farm at Newton in Cambridgeshire at the turn of the century, and although this is a painting, it is no picturesque fiction. Whether oxen inspired the same protective feelings in their keepers as did horses, I am not sure, but the ones I have studied in photographs look well-fed, healthy and comfortable while pulling the plough. At least fen soil put less of a strain on them than heavier high-land soils.

(Cambridgeshire Collection)

TWEECH BURNING

Reclaiming the fens for agriculture was no simple matter. Drained of water for most of the year, the fields remained wet enough to sustain the common reed, which was harvested along with the wheat well into the first half of this century. The huge sheaves coming off Soham Mere in the 1930s. were made heavy with reeds, and sometimes there were enough of them to keep the corn upright during the late heavy storms, which was the only purpose they could serve. Once the water plants had beem eradicated, the dry-surface weeds began to take hold, none more tenacious than tweech which remains a curse today. While ploughing continues behind, using the more conventional means of horses, these fen folk are burning off the tweech while the weather is dry. Scuffling the land after harvest and burning off was the only way to reduce the curse, and it was a light and pleasant job compared to many. This is Robert Farren's depiction of it in the 1870s.

(Author's Collection)

PLOUGHING IN 1917

Pride in workmanship was never far from the minds of farmworkers, even in the hazardous fens where their ploughing skills might be dissolved at any time by flooding. Men were closer to the land in the horse-drawn days, knowing its vagaries and its smell uncontaminated by poisons. There was pride in ploughing most of all, for these were precedents to be upheld, and the furrows must be straight and as perfect as possible. Putting them there, a ploughman walked ten miles a day and, in time, would acquire an unmistakable ploughman's gait. This young man is on The Broads at Burwell in 1917, and there is water lying on the surface behind him. This is deep ploughing, and two horses were needed to make it comfortable for them. Their collars took the strain of pulling, the whippletrees kept the traces apart, and there would be a spud — a straightened hoe — on the plough to clean the share when the land was sticky, as it is becoming here. The ploughmen would have to keep the traces taut on the turn, or they might tangle or irritate the horse. This is the picturesque ploughing we love to remember, but it is hard work, for the man had much manoeuvring to do at the handles, and it was not just a matter of walking along behind.

(Cambridgeshire Collection)

FEN TRACTORS

Tractors were not of immediate use on fen soils. They had to be adapted to stay on the surface as far as possible, and the heavier they became the more essential this was. Using the principal of the first-world-war tank, the crawler tractor was introduced, and there was not much to get in its way. The need for small tractors was obvious, and these could operate better on the light fen soil. Such was this early Bristol crawler tractor manufactured by the Douglas Motorcycle Company in the 1930s, pulling here a Ransome Motrag two-furrow plough on land near Wisbech. Fordson, International and Case were the familiar names on tractors at this time. Once pneumatic tyres were introduced, the crawler tractors lost favour.

(Lilian Ream)

THE HOEING GANG

When gangs were the norm, there was great comradeship among farm workers. Reliance on machines and chemicals, therefore, destroyed a way of life for legions of men — and women — who had anticipated only land work from their school days. Controversy among them certainly spiced their days out on the land, but that was life and the air was clean. This happy gang, taking a moment to lean on their hoes for the photographer, were working in Swaffham Bulbeck, a fen-edge village in Cambridgeshire, early this century. Land jobs were never done and no-one rushed to finish them. Hoeing was a thorough job, for the evidence of bad workmanship was soon showing, and no man wanted a reputation for that. And there was a hoe for every job, the smallest having been worn down to that size, and the handles made perfect leaning sticks when you needed a rest, perhaps to cogitate on some problem at home or abroad, or to wonder what was on the table for dinner.

(Cambridgeshire Collection)

THE DROWNS

There have been many flooding catastrophes in the fens since it was reclaimed for agriculture, and every fen farmer prays to be without one in his working lifetime. There were great fen 'drowns' this century in 1912, 1937 and 1947; this last resulting from the swift thaw following that severe post-war winter. This is just one of many scenes of flooding in the Sutton and Haddenham area in 1947, the farmhouse devastated, the farmyard a separate island, the human and animal occupants gone, the surrounding crops of winter wheat ruined. Fenmen face unobstructed distances. They have seamen's eyes, but they have no wish to be as marine as this — and there was no rejoicing at nature's recovery of the fens.

(Cambridgeshire Collection; W. Martin Lane)

FAREWELL TO THE FARM

There were spare soldiers aplenty to mount a military operation to contend with the fen floods of 1947. They plugged the banks and evacuated the populations to higher ground, they cleaned up the debris and, after the floods had receded, they reported back to the their barracks after a good job well done. That left the farmers to settle back in as best they could, and W. Martin Lane, the Ely amateur photographer, who rushed to many a fen disaster to preserve the moment for posterity on film, has caught to perfection this moment of leaving home with the farm dog on a tumbrel cart, a moment as forlorn as the landscape itself, once the floods had gone. Both these men are young enough to cling to their optimism, and at least we can say there has been no such disaster since.

(Cambridgeshire Collection; W. Martin Lane)

RESCUING THE SHEEP

Water took the lives of many animals in the fens. River banks are good grazing grounds, but the banks are steep in places, and cattle and sheep can lose their hold on them. This is a chance the fen farmer, responsible to an extent for the state of a river bank adjacent to his land, must take, and generally livestock is safe there, but in the case of a 'drown', it can be all hands to the rescue, as depicted here in an old print, where sheep have shifted to the highest ground to become marooned. The floods here are relatively shallow, but those of 1937 and 1947, put there by burst river banks, were much deeper and many animals were lost.

(Cambridgeshire Collection)

HARVESTING WITH BOAT, RAMSEY, AUGUST 1912.

BRINGING IN THE SHEAVES

Now this was uncommon. No proven weather sage such as our own Jim 'Tuddy' Bailey of Wicken, who liked nothing better than to predict against all likelihood, could have anticipated such an untimely flooding as this at the height of the corn harvest. Wheat grew very tall in the fens at that time, and even light rain just before the ripening could lay it flat, forcing a resort to the scythe for bringing it in. But this poor Ramsey farmer is really up against it, needing a boat to replace his wagon or tumbrel. With so much water on his mind he must have added his tears. But this was so unusual that this photograph sold well for picture postcards in and after 1912.

(Cambridgeshire Collection)

PEACOCK FARM

Wicken is strictly a fen-edge village, settled above the waters that once touched it on three sides, where the houses were on safe ground. On one side spreads Soham Mere, now treeless farmland, once a secure resource of fish and wildfowl for the primitive inhabitants. Attempts to drain it began in 1594, but Vermuyden's arrival had the fenmen up in arms, and on 1st May 1637, the local Justices of the Peace were urged to be severe on them. Gradually they lost their source of food, and farmers secured theirs, but water lay on that mere into Victorian times. The road through Wicken is paralleled by its Low Road running along the fringe of the mere, along which were a string of farm houses and cottages under thatch, all of them now gone. Peacock Farm was one of these, the one nearest to the village and the school, keeping us in touch with the seasonal jobs. Bob Taylor was the last owner, a typical fen smallholder of the time, his farmyard with its livestock typically warm and welcoming to those in sympathy. When he sold the house, it was allowed to rot slowly into the ground.

(Author's Collection)

ST JOHN'S FARM

The well-appointed fen farms were built above fen level, close to the towns or on silt islands and rodhams. Those resting on the peat were, more often than not, a collection of ramshackle huts and shelters made of poles and straw, with a cottage on the lean or cracking down the middle, and never very old. 'Leaners' were a familiar sight in the fens until recent times, but many have been replaced now by bungalows built on concrete rafts. The safest houses to live in were made of wood and corrugated iron or asbestos. St John's Farm is in Ely itself, by the original route from Cambridge, following the Roman causeway. It rests on the site of a thirteenth-century separate religious foundation, the history of which is otherwise obscure. It became secular, then a manor house where lived between thirty and forty people, and two of its original buildings remain. Its chapel of St John shows at the centre of this picture taken in the 1930s, and it has been used for many years as a barn, but both buildings are under the watchful eye of English Heritage. Here, however, is a typical farmyard with chickens and weaners free to roam, with the welcoming feel that farmyards once had.

(Cambridgeshire Collection)

THE BLOWS

Trouble when wet, trouble when dry: the high winds of spring and sometimes autumn can blow the peatlands away like powder, ripping up the sowings of sugar beet, filling the ditches, blacking out the sun, even sifting through the window panes. Any man trying to work out there would be chasing his cap, wiping his eyes and soon going home looking like a chimney sweep. As this century progressed, the fen farmers made things worse for themselves by removing trees and hedges as if they never belonged there, the chainsaw and heavy machinery making this easy for them. Today, in anticipation of 'blows', they implant straw between the rows of some salad plants, but trees have been put back — in serried ranks, regulating the vistas still further. This view on the Isleham–Prickwillow road in 1955 tells all.

(Wisbech Advertiser — Fenland Citizen)

WHERE SHEEP MAY SAFELY GRAZE

History was enacted here where Hereward the Wake resisted the Norman invaders. We are down on fen level at Aldreth Causeway, where peace reigns in the 1930s, where one farmer's small flock of sheep are moving from one feeding ground to another. Three times Hereward repelled the Conqueror's men near this spot, setting fire to the reeds, forcing the Normans to build a causeway to enable them to shift the 'last of the English' from his stronghold. It was called Lindon then, but eventually the wastes that thwarted William became rich farmland where serenity such as this could reign. Small flocks of sheep like this were the norm at this time.

(Cambridgeshire Collection; Briscoe Snelson)

SHEEP WASHING

Full-time shepherds managed large flocks of sheep on some farms, but many smallholders had a few sheep as part of their livestock when there was plenty of natural grazing for them in pastures, and on the washes and river banks. These they could manage without trouble, although they might need a skilled shearer for the wool. Before shearing them, they needed to be washed, and the simplest way was to dip them in the river after they had been grazing the banks. The scene is Stretham Ferry in the 1920s, and the men are laundering vigorously. Sheep, needless to say, with their covering, were not keen on immersion. While wading to drink, they might easily get stuck in the mud, and sometimes they were washed away, and I have seen them floating down the river feet upwards.

(Cambridgeshire Collection)

SHEEP DIPPING

Sprucing up the fleece before shearing was one thing, but there was more to keeping the outside of a sheep in trim than washing in water. Sheep-dipping has for long been essential to the good health and comfort of sheep, and where there was a large flock, such as here early this century in Swaffham Prior, Cambridgeshire, on the estate of Charles Ambrose, the dipping pen was a permanent structure, ensuring that the sheep had nowhere to go but through the chemical pool. The fleeces concealed ticks and keds, and flies left their maggots behind. Those who kept only a few sheep simply dipped them in troughs.

(Cambridgeshire Collection)

SHEEP-FEED

In early spring it was the custom for some farmers to drive their sheep across their fields of winter wheat, cropping them enough to encourage a stronger second growth. 'The Royal Hoof', they called this treatment, which also fertilized the soil. Large flocks of sheep needed more than the available pastures to keep them fed, and kale was a crop grown for them. This crop is at Bottisham near Cambridge in February 1933, and the shepherds have arrived with hurdles to fence it off. The monotonous diet would be down to the ground before the sheep tired of it. Until November 1894, Bottisham and Lode were one village, with a station in what is still known as Bottisham Fen. The line served villages between Cambridge and Mildenhall in Suffolk.

(Cambridgeshire Collection)

THE LAMBING FOLD

Only stumps of the kale remain, the lambing fold has been set up in Bottisham, and long nights of vigil are on for the two shepherds, so concerned for safe healthy deliveries. The fold would have served already as a shelter in midwinter, but only the ewes are now in residence. Shepherds were watchful men. Sheep could roll on to their backs and not be able to get up without assistance, and could worry themselves to death, with sheep-worrying by dogs always possible when there were so many on the loose at that time. In earlier times, sheep stealing was rife. It was a relatively easy animal to corner and kill noiselessly, and many a fen farmer suffered losses this way. Men were still being hanged for stealing sheep into the nineteenth century, but reprieve with an alternative sentence of deportation, when fines were so seldom payable, became the norm.

(Cambridgeshire Collection)

LIVESTOCK IN TOWN

Townsfolk breathed much the same air as countryfolk at the time of this scene nearly two hundred years ago. Horse traffic kept the atmosphere strong, and one small farmer with his cow and a few sheep on their way to or from a common grazing ground made little difference. Animals travelled only on foot, to and from the market and between farms or pastures, and there was nothing to disturb the tutors or students at work, hopefully, behind those ancient walls. This is Trumpington Street, Cambridge, with St Peter's (Peterhouse) College on the left, and apart from the animals and dress, the scene is not radically different today. And to this day, sheep and cattle graze the meadows behind The Backs.

(Cambridgeshire Collection)

THE FAMILY

Fidelity is not in the nature of the bovine male, so the photographer here creates a false picture of a settled family. It was an unusual opportunity she could not resist, bravely standing her ground before the bull. The scene is Desborough's Station Farm in Wisbech St Mary in the 1960s, and if the bull is the father of the calf, he is the father of many others off camera. There was no economic sense in a small farmer keeping a bull for his three or four cows, and one bull would serve a wide area, being led there by a rope through the ring in his nose. A pretty scene though.

(Lilian Ream)

THE COWMAN

The riverside washes, and in particular those between the Old and New Bedford Rivers, designed to carry the overflow in the wet season, were ideal grazing places in summer, unless they were being left for hay. Flooding there kept the scrub down, and some farmers had big herds on them with pens by the access roads for taking them away to market or for slaughter. Self-sufficiency, as far as possible, had to be the aim of those many small isolated fen farmers, and each usually had cows enough to provide him with milk and butter, and excess for the pig-swill. After the evening milking, the last job of the day was to turn the milk through the separator, and I last heard one of those humming its evening tune in an isolated farm cottage near Coveney, Ely, in the late 1960s, owned by Ebenezer Barker. I was taken into the cottage one day — into a time capsule. Bigger farmers employed cowmen, and Louis Bailey, seen here in the 1940s, was the cowman born and bred, working for Woollard and Wilfred Barton at Orwell Farm, Wicken. You could set your watch to his daily walks to and from the farm, always allowing that he might have to get up in the night to attend a calving.

(M.R. Barton)

PIGS

In the mixed farming days, pigs were as integral to the cycle and to the economy as cows and chickens, each farmer having only what he could manage, and manage to feed from his own produce, or its equivalent coming back from the mills in concentrated form. He might breed pigs or buy piglets from the market, using up some commodities, such as buttermilk and poor potatoes — cooked — that might otherwise be wasted. He would grow a small crop of mangel-wurzels too, for his livestock, a marvellously economic feedstuff that is now disregarded. The huge red and orange roots would be lifted in the autumn and put into clamps under straw and earth for winter use, ensuring freshness out of season. In the cause of self-sufficiency, the farmer might have one of his pigs slaughtered now and then, to salt the meat down and hang his own hams. Many pigs had the freedom we see here at Pond Green, Wicken, in the 1920s, although the rooting had to be restricted by rings. This is a Large Black sow and the hog was a Large White, producing a disappointing litter for Vincent Towell, who was a local shopkeeper-turned-pig-breeder who employed Robert Porter to take charge. Most fen farmers up to this time had a liking for lard and pork cheeses.

(Kathleen Towell)

THE CHICKENS

They came in all patterns from the original Rhode Island, Leghorn, Brighton Rock and Sussex stock, and they could do much to feed themselves on what was left on the ground in the stackyards and on the stubbles, although there was plenty of tail corn to throw to them twice a day. Where the rooster was in charge as much as the farmer, the hens, as often as not, were left to procreate by deception, emerging at last from their hidden corners and clumps of weeds, all puffed up and proud with a cheeping brood sure of a welcome. They were seldom counted, or even identified, unless they had a limp or one eye — for every farm had its Nelson. Wives and children collected the eggs, a few in nesting boxes, more on high and deep under where the attempted deception was discovered in time. Poultry and duck farms became part of life in the broad fields of Norfolk, but chickens otherwise were integral to any farm which would have been a dead place without them. They worshipped the sun and were home and beauty as this affectionate photograph shows. They were the least confined creatures on any farm, and shutting them in heated sheds with false nightfalls and dawns to make them lay themselves to death was unthinkable. This is Bill Bailey's smallholding in Wicken in the 1920s, and no doubt he had a few cockerels to fatten up for Christmas, and enough eggs left over from his own needs for the fortnightly visit of the egg man, and that, in all conscience, was enough — along with the chicken pies!

(Dorothy Johnson)

TURKEYS

The turkey was a rare sight in the farmyards of my childhood, and few of us had ever tasted its meat before leaving school. The goose had long been the preferred dish for the festive season, for those prepared to forego the traditional beef. Between the wars, turkeys began to proliferate on Norfolk farms as a diversification, until rearing them on a large scale became a separate industry. Never an active bird in captivity, they could keep close company in huge turkey sheds and remain quite healthy, and their meat has become ever more popular all the year round. These, on a small Norfolk farm in 1932, are the richly-flavoured Norfolk Bronze turkeys still in favour on a huge scale.

(Lilian Ream)

GEESE

Few fen farms were without geese, although seldom in great numbers. They were the traditional providers of feathers, eggs, flesh and fat, and together they were louder than any dog at the approach of strangers. They would feed well on what nature provided, were good for cropping the river banks, and were an economic miracle. They could become aggressive too, and children often had to flee from them. Where there was a pond or river, they would never stray far, and they are as settled here in the centre of a village as they would be on an isolated farm. These geese are by the Well Creek in Upwell in the 1890s, just glancing at the passer-by who completely disregards them. We live in a fat-conscious age, so the goose is less in demand for the Christmas table.

(Cambridgeshire Collection)

POTATOES

It was soon proven that vegetables grew best in the vegetable soil of the fens. Turnips yielded well in the early days, but latterly the area has become a huge resource of potatoes, grown larger and more plentifully than anywhere else in the land — even more so since irrigation was seen to be essential to huge tonnages. Today they are planted and harvested with machines, but both jobs once provided hard work for many people, so many of them women looking for this seasonal employment. This picture shows that as late as 1947 they were still planted and gathered by hand, testing the backbone for hours on end. Where farmers grew potatoes only for their own use, they planted a few rows across a headland, as near to home a possible, always doing the job on Good Friday for a certain yield. Then the bending was repeated for the lifting and a clamp made for the winter. The Norfolk bonnet, worn here at Soham, was in use much later than this. Indeed, it was set aside only when there was no longer the need to plant or harvest by hand.

(Cambridgeshire Collection)

POTATO PICKERS

Potato planting and picking, fruit picking and sugar beet singling were all on the calendar for those women who, while having plenty to do at home, wanted to cash in on these short seasonal jobs. They were happy to do it, liking the company and the fresh air away from the hot stove that had to be there all the year round. These potato pickers are at Keating's Tiptree Farm in Swaffham Fen, Cambridgeshire, and the man with the horse is Mr Littlechild. The four women, left to right, are: Bertha Bailey of Wicken and next to her a traveller timing her visit to coincide with the work, Mrs Fred Diver and Dorothy Bailey, both of Wicken, in the year 1925. Pails were preferred here to the old osier baskets that had been used for centuries.

(Author's Collection)

THE POTATO SPINNER

The mechanical age has arrived early on in this potato field near Cambridge in the 1920s. For other farmers the horse-drawn spinner remained a novelty for much longer, and many were into the tractor age before resorting to such a device. Beforehand, the plough was used to lift the potatoes and the harrow would rake a few more to the surface after the first picking, for nothing then was wasted. Today's potatoes have to be in prime condition for marketing — many flawed ones are left lying on the fields.

(Cambridgeshire Collection)

HAULING THEM HOME

Today the potato tops are killed off artificially before the lifting, which can then be brought forward before the land is sticky. At the time of this photograph, taken near Prickwillow in the 1920s, the land could be in a very soggy state for the potato harvest, and hauling them off the land in a wagon would need four horses like this to be certain of progress. They have arrived here on the hard road, when it will be much easier. Big farms with huge acreages of potatoes began harvesting them early between the wars. In August/September 1934, on Letter F Farm in Burnt Fen, twenty-one acres of King Edward potatoes yielded three-hundred-and-nineteen tons, six hundredweights.

(Cambridgeshire Collection)

THE POTATO GRAVE

When grown in such vast quantities, the ideal way to store potatoes was the clamp, hale, pie or grave, as they preferred in Norfolk, and they were a feature of the flat landscape from October, diminishing as the contents were riddled for the markets. Today the potatoes are tipped into dark sheds, although a clamp is sometimes made by a small farmer. Straw-covered, with earth sealing it down, dug from a surrounding trench that also served for drainage, the clamp keeps the potatoes in good condition for a long time. Here the drainage is served by a dyke, but it is unlikely the potatoes had to be conveyed across the plank. The scene is Smeeth Road, Norfolk, in 1929.

(Lilian Ream)

RIDDLING POTATOES

There is the story of the American servicemen who, while more intent to show off his fine car, drew up to talk to a group of fenmen riddling potatoes He gazed as if in wonder at the sheer size of the potatoes and complimented the men. Then, more befitting the role of the boastful Yank so often quoted in the fens, he added that they grew much bigger potatoes in his land. 'Ah, ' said one worker with quiet disdain. 'We grow 'em to fit our own mouths round here.' When potatoes came to be grown on a commercial scale, the riddling machine became a blessing. The first models were operated by hand, and this engine-driven one in Burnt Fen, near Prickwillow, Cambridgeshire, in the 1920s, has long been obsolete. Today one machine does the lifting and riddling, but sorters ride on them and a fair labour force is still necessary

(Cambridgeshire Collection)

CELERY

Celery today means fen celery, with tender white stalks out of the black peat, crisp as frost, grown in great quantities for a discriminating market. Here on Letter F Farm at Burnt Fen in 1941, the demand is well established at a time when tractor and horses were working side by side on equal terms, as they would be for a few years longer. Here they are drawing trenches, spreading fertilizer and making the trenches firm for planting the celery by hand. It would be moulded up later to produce those long white stems, and the wetter the season the better. Today the crop is soon subjected to irrigation to speed the growth, and some self-bleaching celery is grown on the flat

(Cambridgeshire Collection)

THE PLANTINGS

Here, on the same day in 1941, you can see where the trench has been pressed down to receive the dibber, and the man has a monotonous day ahead of him. The lady has the slightly easier job, and for her it was another of those brief seasonal jobs over and above the household chores, and very welcome too for the household economy. Today fewer of her kind are needed in the celery fields where the machine has largely taken over. The first planting machines were used in Lincolnshire for planting cauliflowers, but they were easily adapted for celery. A man rode on the early models dropping the plants in the holes, but the passenger today simply feeds the machine, which plants and compresses behind it. We live in what might be termed the salad age, and the fens grow lettuces in great quantity and to a big size, the first plantings being brought along under polythene. The human hand is still a sophisticated tool and many hands are still needed to tend and bring in the salad crops of the fens, including beetroot, parsnips, fennel and, of course, onions.

(Cambridgeshire Collection)

HARVESTING THE CELERY

It is October 1934, and at that time many an autumn tea-table would be crowned by celery stalks poking out of a tall jar, and the eating could be noisy. I still cannot regard it as an all-the-year-round vegetable. We are back at Letter F Farm, and three horses are needed to draw a relatively light load off the soft land. The celery could be eased out of the soil with ploughs, but the rest was hand work, and the air was spicy for weeks . At the horse's head stands E. Benstead, and next to the trailer is G. Benstead. The farmer was H.G.S. Wilson, but Letter F is a Frederick Hyam farm today. And today the miracle machine lifts, tops, washes and packs the celery in one operation, and the labour force on the fields and in the packing stations has been reduced, but that is the world we live in.

(Cambridgeshire Collection)

CARROTS

Do they grow them anywhere else, you might ask when crossing the fens today? They are grown thickly, yet to a size huge enough to make gardeners envious. Some are left in the soil all winter, with enough of that soil drawn over them to keep out the frosts which can reduce them to jelly. The big growers select and pack their own for the market, making work for many, but the labour of lifting has gone. When they were picked by hand, the job was done in the autumn, and the autumn we see here was 1917, with young men conspicuous by their absence at war, and the place is Doddington near Chatteris. Resting awhile for the camera are, left to right, back: G. Behagg, H. Beard, W. Jackson, D. Hudson, H. Curtis, E. Gray, E. Lanton, F. Gidson, J. Hart and D. Norman. Middle: Mrs Behagg, F. Watkinson, Mrs Beard, Mrs Whittaker, W. Clark, M. Durham, Mrs Wilmoy. Front: H. Jackson, B. Curtis, M. Manton, W. Dack and G. Gidson. The war and its casualties must have been the first and last topic of conversation. Doddington, once the largest parish in Cambridgeshire, sits on an island, second only in size to Ely, but only twenty-five feet above sea level.

(Cambridgeshire Collection)

SUGAR BEET

It was grown as a vegetable long before the first attempts to extract sugar from it 1747. Russia built the first factory in 1803. By 1880 the tonnage of beet sugar worldwide had surpassed that of cane sugar, yet production in England developed only after the first world war, expanding rapidly from the mid-1920s. Fen farmers soon realised the potential of the crop, and factories were built to process it. They were soon irked by the permit system that still operates, ensuring a steady supply to the factories for the four-month 'campaigns'. However, the harvesting of the crop was slow and laborious for a long time, keeping the men on the land into midwinter, and they could not at first have exceeded their quota based on the acreage grown. The first means of lifting the crop was a two-tined fork. The digger shed the earth against the handle, and laid the root flat for chopping and tossing into heaps or rows, as we see here in 1934 near Wisbech. Men were given piecework wages to do this, and they liked it better than the double pay for the long hours of the corn harvest. The beet were then tossed into tumbrels and tipped by the hard roads or rivers for easy access by lorries and barges. The beet plough was soon introduced to lift the roots, and after the second world war came the mechanical beet harvesters that made the lifting easy. The crops grow heavier in the fens than anywhere else, and are integral to the landscape

(Lilian Ream)

EASING THE LABOUR

The road transport firms were boosted by the arrival of sugar beet. Three- and five-ton lorries were used at first to take the beet to the factories, and the drivers provided a welcome news service for the farm workers as they loaded the lorries together. Using what breath they had to spare as they filled the lorry, using those scoop-shaped forks with blunted tines, the talk became lively and often frivolous. But well before loading devices for sugar beet were considered necessary, this farmer at Grange Farm, near Stretham Ferry, brought in this dragline for the purpose. The year is 1928 and the time had not arrived for pneumatic tyres to ease the passage of the lorries. Roots tumbled off them as they vibrated their way to the factories, creating a hazard for cyclists after dark.

(Cambridgeshire Collection)

A SMOOTHER JOURNEY

The sugar beet factories at King's Lynn and Ely were served by the Great Ouse as well as by road and rail, and sugar beet boosted the barge traffic for a long time. These neatly-aligned barges loaded with beet are at Wiggenhall St Germans in 1933, on their way to Lynn, providing a smooth journey, but needing much labour to load on and off. One small powered boat could pull these barges with ease, but gradually all the haulage was transferred to the roads. The lorries drove on to a weighbridge, but the beet had to be taken off the barges for weighing.

(Lilian Ream)

THE FACTORY

The beet-harvesting season begins in September, when the beet leaves are still green and growing, continuing into late January unless a particularly severe winter prolongs it. Today a large field of beet can be cleared in hours by the mechanical harvesters and the trailers alongside, in which case the roots are piled into vast heaps for delivery as the permits allow. This gets them off the land before the soggy weather make it difficult; whereas, in the old days, when frozen fingers or wet feet were part of the job of lifting, the sight of bogged-down tumbrels being hauled out by two horses, with a man spading the mud off the wheels, was all too familiar. Soon the sour air hanging over the beet fields would be pervaded by a syrupy sweetness issuing from the beet factory, steaming there in the distance like a huge pleasure liner. With its heavy production, the fen country needed those nearby factories, but they are still in the process of being reduced. Lynn's has been scheduled for closure, but this one at Ely, opened in 1925, closed in 1972, making those at Bury St Edmunds and Wissington, Norfolk, the nearest for the local farmers. Ben Lee of Queen Adelaide, the site of the factory, stands in the barge.

(Cambridgeshire Collection)

ASPARAGUS

Fen farmers who have increasingly become market gardeners have never taken to growing asparagus on a large scale. Machines cannot enter into it, since the crop must be cut as it grows for about seven weeks in spring and early summer. It was, and is, a small grower's crop, yielding a good income for its short season, but occupying a lot of space with its wide rows for the rest of the year. Weeding it was also a tiresome job, but chemicals keep the weeds down today. On the fruit orchards between Wicken and Soham earlier this century, asparagus was grown between the trees, and this scene is also in Burwell Fen, in the 1920s. The grower was smallholder Morley Hawes, whose wife Helena is holding the bunches here. Her daughter Amy sits left, and her grandchild Frances Dring squeezes into the picture while the kettle boils. Great pride was taken in the quality of the asparagus grown, and a prize bunch was often the reason for a picture being taken. In season there is a huge demand for it straight from the grower and Morley Hawes and his family could never cut it fast enough from their six acres of beds.

(Author's Collection)

HAY TIME

Sweetness pervaded the air when the hay harvest got under way in June, a smell that may well have oppressed the horses involved, since they knew it to be a prelude to the more exacting corn harvest. By habit they began to cling to the far end of their pastures when the horsekeepers took halters to them in the morning. Cutting the hay was all man's work at first, until the coming of the grass cutter, comfortably pulled by two mares. The scene is near Wicken Fen in 1917, with Reg Butcher aboard working for his uncle, Morley Hawes (right), with Reg's father Robert behind him with two visitors. If rain intervened, the hay might have to be forked or horseraked over, or if it was already in cocks these would have to be opened up to dry. Later the horse-drawn spinners came into service, and the stacks perfumed the stackyards, even through the corn harvest. Then they were cut like cake as they were needed for the racks, and when the next hay time came, the old hay would be good for little but farmer's lung.

(Author's Collection)

CARTING THE HAY

This could be harder than the cutting — for the pitcher, at least, although the unloader in the stackyard would eventually be forking it high too. The sun, however, was a blessing, enabling them to get the job done quickly, for it was never a prolonged harvest. In Wicken, Louis Bailey is forking it up to Billy Norman, while Tom Bailey takes charge of the horse, no doubt getting his hand in for the later horseleading. They are working for Woollard Barton in the 1930s, and Rip the dog is on hand for anything small and furry bolting from his path.

(M.R. Barton)

CUTTING THE CORN

Stone-age man used a sharpened flint, and the ancient Egyptians the jawbone of a large animal, sharpening the teeth into a cutting edge. The first sickles were made of hard wood, often with a handle of baked clay, but by the middle ages the first scythes had been introduced with long handles to reduce the bending. There followed the cradle scythe, fixed with a willow bow to bunch the corn tidily to the swinging action, and these were used until the combine harvesters came along — but only to cut lanes around the corn for the entrance of the self-binder. The reaper preceded that after the first horse-drawn cutters were patented in the early nineteenth century. How tall the wheat grew in the fens until our time — unless the weather laid it flat, which was often. This mower last century was lucky to find crisp standing corn. He knew how to conserve his energy, keeping the blade sharp from the rub in his belt or pocket, using it like a tribal drummer, and cutting a broad swathe to fetch the corn down like icicles, leaving the air spiced with shorn coltsfoot, cornmint and poppy. The air would dry soon enough with all that straw about him for weeks.

(Cambridgeshire Collection)

THE BINDERS

There would be plenty of time to feed the livestock in the morning, for the damp had to go off the land before they could make a start with the cutting. Then, to the innocent observer, the beckoning arms of the reaper or the serenely turning sails of the self-binder would complete a charming prospect. As here in 1929 near Wisbech, where a man takes a ride in the sun on a reliable machine behind proudly-kept horses, shaping an ordered landscape about him. In truth it was an anxious, rigorous time for all involved, not least the horses who were pestered with flies and midges during the long torrid days, and would finish racked, foaming with sweat and striped by their harness. The local blacksmith or mechanic would have maintained the machine beforehand, but breakdowns were common, and the rider would be on edge for this. There would be twelve-hour days for a good six weeks of harvest on most farms, where the aim would be to finish the cutting before the carting began — and only stockmen worked on Sundays. As the last swathes of corn fell, there would be men and dogs on hand to shoot and catch the rabbits, and everybody would be eating harvest rabbit with their spuds and runner beans.

(Lilian Ream)

TRACTOR POWER

It had come to this much earlier than the preceding photograph on some well-appointed farms, but horses were in constant use well after the Second World War. The scene is near Burwell in the early 1920s, and tractors were to undergo many modifications before the combine harvester arrived. Power-binders came in, driven as well as pulled by the tractor, and horses gradually came to have an easier time until they were replaced altogether. Gradually too the machine smells became inseparable from harvest and life on the land altogether, and such a tractor as this would evoke acute nostalgia in those who remembered its arrival. Indeed, we shall come to regard combines with deepening affection, although it is hard to imagine what will supersede them.

(Cambridgeshire Collection; Dorothy Grainger)

THE COMBINES

The combine harvesters had long been a fixture on the broad plains of the United States, Canada and Australia before they arrived in Britain. Sunshine Grain Harvesters were manufactured in Australia by a subsidiary company of Massey-Harris in the 1930s, and both self-binders and combines were imported in increasing numbers during the late 1930s. and the Second World War. Fields had to be enlarged for them, and thus the fens lost so many of their hedges, and the farmer no longer appeared the countryman. The first combines were not self-powered, but, like this one near Wisbech in the late 1950s, were hauled by tractors. This is a caterpillar combine harvester, hauled by a caterpillar diesel fifty tractor where the wheat has taken a blasting from the rain, which would have worried the farmer a lot more a few years earlier. Today's sophisticated combines, that offer clean comfort to the drivers, can cost around £130,000, making you wonder why the buyer chose not to keep the money and retire

(Lilian Ream)

BRINGING IN THE SHEAVES

There was hardly a village boy who was not involved in the corn harvest in one way or another, be it in a playful, hunting or working capacity, in the day of sheaves and stacks. Friends were deserted, as families took precedence bringing in the sheaves. A boy might first offer to lead the horse from shock to shock on the land, but the pitcher could as well do this for himself. The traditional cry of 'Hold, ye!' rose from the stubbles as the boy soon learned to warn the loader before leading the horse on. The pitcher's job was hard, as was the unloader's in the stackyard when the stack rose above him. Louis Bailey, here at Orwell Farm, Wicken, in the 1930s, is unloading bean sheaves which were heavy enough, but wheatsheaves off the fen level were heavier still. While the roof of the stack was being built, there was another tough job for the man in the 'chairhole' who had little room for leverage and was trapped in an oven as he strained the sheaves high. Barley stood a long time on the shock, since it had to be bone dry, but it made light carting, and the only problem was its fast company of thistles and the creeping awns that could madden your skin or even get in your eyes and mouth. Oats, peas, mustard and buckwheat were the other crops contributing to new settlements of golden temples, and terraces every year, soon under shining thatch, soon cosily occupied by rats and mice, slowly to give way to demolition throughout the winter and into spring.

(M.R. Barton)

84

THE STACKS

They were the fulfilment of the farming year. Ricks they might have been elsewhere, where they also had stooks rather than shocks, but in the fens they were always, and ever will be, stacks. They embodied the farmer's pride and success, and they had to stand proud. Scruffy stacks badly constructed, soon on the lean and supported by props, were shaming, and good farmers had no time for those who did not care about this. The thatch had to look perfect and decorative corn dollies did nobody any harm. They were part of a way of life, and it is sad they had to go out of fashion to leave the stackyards drab or soon covert by huge sheds for huge machines — or even ploughed up. Space there was at a premium, and many stacks were built on the land, while the bigger farmers threshed a lot of their corn off the shock. These stacks at Littleport in the 1930s. could hardly be bettered. The last corn stacks I saw were at Oxlode, Pymoor, near Ely in 1964, and the farmer later confirmed they were the last he built. I still miss them in the landscape.

(Cambridgeshire Collection)

THE GLEANERS

The combines did away with the ritual customs that followed harvest. After the horserake had gone over the stubbles and the rakings were tipped against the stacks for the threshing machines, the gleaners' bell rang from the churches, and, unless two sheaves had been left in the land to warn them off, all were free to pick up the fallen ears for their backyard fowls. Finally the mobile huts were drawn to the stubbles where the chickens could feast off the spilled grain for a fortnight or more; thus nothing was wasted and there were few grains of corn to interfere with the following crop. The last gleaners' bell to ring in Cambridgeshire was at Balsham in the 1920s, and now there is nothing to glean. These gleaners at Bottisham, Cambridgeshire, in the 1880s, have mobilised themselves for their share, and it was something they depended upon. Children between the wars would find gleaning fun for a short while, the girls making fronds of the ears to show up the ham-fisted boys.

(Cambridgeshire Collection)

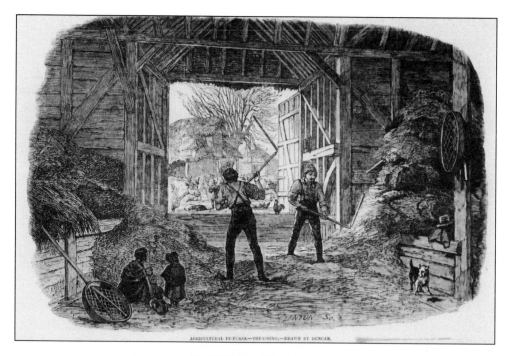

AGRICULTURAL PICTURES.—THRASHING.—DRAWN BY DUNCAN.

FLAILING THE CORN

Only the combines took the hard work out of threshing, or thrashing as the fenmen always called it. Later it was as often called steaming, but before the threshing machines came along, the first of them turned by hand and causing unrest among laid-off landworkers, the steam all came out of the men threshing with flails. It was not an unskilled job to use those flails to full effect, but then farmyards were full of offensive weapons if you regarded them as such. The flail was a tool that remained on the farm long after it was in general use, to thresh a few rakings or perhaps clover or sangfoine grown on a small patch of spare ground. Shaking and winnowing were equal parts of threshing with flails.

(Cambridgeshire Collection)

STEAM THRESHING

Once the hand-manipulated threshing machines had gone, the shape of the threshing engine soon resolved itself, and it underwent only slight modifications over many years. The same can be said of the threshing drum, or mill as they were sometimes called, and the straw jack that in the fens was always referred to as the jackstraw. The composite word for the three machines together was the threshing tackle, and here in Pymoor we have the familiar scene of all work, steam and dust until the engine was stopped and there was a blissful, sizzling silence for the food breaks. With those slight engine modifications, the scene was the same until the Second World War when the tractor took the place of the steam engine. Farmers threshed as they could dispose of the grain, for there was no other way to store but in sacks, and these must not be left in the barns long or the rats would gnaw through them. On the drum was the sheaf-cutter and the feeder, and down below the chaff-boy and a man taking off the grain in sacks at the engine end. He would weigh the corn into combs equalling eighteen stones for wheat, sixteen for barley and twelve for oats, and the farmer would cart them to the barn or granary. Threshing this way is still done today, but only to ensure good straw for thatching.

(Cambridgeshire Collection)

THE WAR YEARS

There was never a spare farmhand on any small fenland farm, but when the farmer had more than one son working with him he was, in spite of his indispensability, in danger of losing one of them to the armed services during the two world wars. The immediate loss would mean nothing compared to the possibility of losing him for good, but another pair of hands would be needed, and they usually belonged to the fair sex. Thousands joined the Women's Land Army during both world wars to supply just such assistance, and for many this was their first experience of life on the land. But the majority knew what to expect, and they did a good job while looking as picturesque as this First World War milkmaid posing for the family at home. Not all the jobs were as comfortable as this, and the farmers made sure they did their share.

(Cambridgeshire Collection)

ALL FAIR HANDS TO THE STOCKYARD

All land army girls had their walking-out uniform, but they never quite sacrificed their identity when doing the various jobs about the farm and on land. The caps and coats here during the First World War remind you they are not local farmers' wives and daughters, but servicewomen enjoying their own company, smiling for the families at home. They soon sacrificed any illusions about farm work, however, and were well and truly hardened to it when the wars came to an end. Very few of them chose to continue working on the land. The men may have enjoyed working in their company, but working beside women had been nothing new to them.

(Cambridgeshire Collection)

THE UNOFFICIAL LAND ARMY

Not all those new women helpers on the land during the First World War were enlisted for this purpose. Many were the genteel ladies living nearby who would not normally have depended on such work, and what they could not do with any confidence individually, they could often do together. It was, it has to be said, a show of patriotism not backed up by a willingness to break sweat, and you cannot believe very strongly in the will of these women to do a full day's work. In unsoiled dresses they stand by a load of hay, letting their act be recorded while the man panders to them willingly. The man on the load is either avoiding the camera or afraid of being shaken off the load by an inexperienced handler of horses — or hay-forks!

(Cambridgeshire Collection)

THE WORKING PRISONERS

Eventually during the Second World War, another work-force came to the aid of fen farmers and farmers everywhere. These are Italian prisoners of war riddling potatoes on a fen farm in 1944, outnumbering the farmer by four to one. Whether they had been experienced at it or not, they settled into this temporary way of life very comfortably after the hazardous service they had known. They were well fed and able to fraternize, and many left carrying happy memories of their days in England. Home came the British servicemen to replace them, but it was not long before the new age in farming made many of them redundant.

(Lilian Ream)

A ROYAL VISIT

During the Second World War, the War Agricultural Committee was concerned not only to facilitate the transportation of produce from the fens by the laying concrete surfaces over the old droves, but to find new land to grow more food. They earmarked Adventurers' Fen in Burwell Fen, where the abandoned peat diggings had become a waterlogged paradise for wildfowl, for reclamation. The land had been purchased in 1939 by nurseryman Alan Bloom, who was to write a book about reclaiming the bogs for the WAG. It was a laborious task using crawler tractors, but eventually it was done to the detriment of wildlife, but to the advantage of the nation. The accomplishment was acknowledged by the King and Queen in 1942 when they visited the site and met the workers after travelling by barge along Burwell Lode.

(Cambridgeshire Collection)

THE MILKMAN

The village milkmen were simply farmers who kept more cows than average, fitting in a daily round with pony and cart before making a start on the land. They carried the milk in a churn and people brought their own jugs to them. Many homes were supplied by farmworkers bringing milk home from the farm, and the milkman's round never took long. Also, should they run short or their milk curdle in high summer, people knew where they could buy an extra pennyworth of full cream or a ha'p'orth of skimmed. Dairy farms supplied the towns, and the cart shown here was most convenient for going from door to door. Here the Wisbech Dairy Farmers' Company, in the 1930s, are between the ages of providing from the churn or in the sealed bottles we know today.

(Lilian Ream)

THE BLACKSMITH

It was once said that a good wheelwright would never be without a job, but if that is no longer true it can still be said of the blacksmith, there being so few of them today. Iron-bending machines and mechanical hammers are now part of their equipment, but it was all done by iron hands in the old days when the blacksmith was almost entirely at the service of farmers, and a friend indeed. This one is George Watts shaping a horseshoe at his Cannon Forge at 21 Horsefair, Wisbech, in the 1930s, with only just enough space to work between hearth and anvil. Blacksmiths were generally kind gentle men, all their natural aggression being expended in their work, but they were not always treated well by their clients. Old and obsolete implements were brought back time and again until there was little he could do to hold them together, and those who were that poor often failed to pay. The pressure on the blacksmith was great, and he often bad to work late hours, even allowing his forge to become an evening centre for resting workers

(Lilian Ream)

THE FARRIER

He was, of course, more often than not one and the same, and this is George Watts again, a few years on, applying the shoe to the horse on the right. No farrier could afford to turn work away, and wet days could become a purgatory for him when so many farmers, unable to get on the land, would choose, without warning, to take their horses for shoeing. Clutching wet fetlocks for hours on end could leave the farrier sore and chapped for weeks, for he could never work freely with adequate waterproof covering, shifting from anvil to horse without a second to spare. Having lost one leg to the farrier, some horses, enjoying their day off, liked to lean on him like an old pal, and the man was going to need his rest that night. Most farriers had been kicked in their time, but recalcitrant horses were rare.

(Lilian Ream)

THE MILLER

Self-sufficiency meant villagers eating bread and cakes from the bakery beside the mill, using flour produced there from the village cornfields. This applied to many villages up to the First World War and a few after, although less so to fen-level villages lacking the necessary elevation. Here, nearer the turn of the century, we see that glorious self-sufficiency functioning in Emneth near Wisbech, courtesy of the last miller there, James Frederick Racey. He and his employees milled the flour, baked the bread and cakes, delivered them by pony and cart, and delivered the flour and meal farther afield in wagons. This mill, built in 1832, suffered a fire in 1912 that destroyed the sails, but Racey had the mill raised six feet and installed a gas engine to power it for several more years. The mill was demolished, but the shop was extended into a general store. Many mills, like that in my village, ended their days of service grinding only meal for livestock. Our last miller limited the farmers to eight sacks of corn at a time, requesting an extra empty sack with them, since the meal would not fit into eight. From the original weight, four pounds per sack were deducted for loss in dust. Our mill, happily, is being brought back to full working order.

(Lilian Ream)

THE SOFT FRUIT SEASON

Fruit picking began with the soft fruit, much of it going to the canning factories These gatherers in a sunny scene from the 1930s look a lot happier than sunbathers, but the wise among them are wearing gloves, for the bushes could be cruel on the fingers. Raspberries and currants were much kinder, but they needed careful handling and, of cource, the low bushes and canes entailed a lot of bending and kneeling. It was very much a woman's job, but the company was jolly and the days flew by. So often the bushes were grown between plum trees, as here, utilising the space, but giving both enough of it to thrive. The quantity of fruit grown in the region is indicated by the fact that the first canning factory in England was built in Wisbech.

(Lilian Ream)

STRAWBERRIES

The luscious strawberry, its popularity enhanced originally by so short a fruiting season, found its natural home in the fens. Once established there to grow abundantly the acreage extended into a burgeoning industry employing legions of casual workers, sweetening the midsummer days like nothing before. They were not there merely for the picking for the crop had to be nurtured along and kept clean, and the straw had to be laid. Such gangs are no longer part of the fen scene. The times have changed for the worse for the fruit growers of the fens, for strawberries are imported all the year round. The remaining beds are largely given over to 'pick your own' customers to save overheads, and while the air is still perfumed by the juice here and there, the good days of supply and ready demand are over. This scene near Wisbech comes from the first decade of this century.

(Cambridgeshire Collection)

APPLES

The sea of apple blossom that once spread over the plains of the North Cambridgeshire fens has been drained away by economic forces. Where orchards remain they consist of Bramley trees pruned to a uniform shape, enabling the apples to be picked from the ground. Blossom still transforms them in spring, but in winter they are not a pretty sight. An industry involving legions of full-time and casual workers, including those at the canning factories, has been decimated, and the land lies forlorn with its set-aside patches. Between the wars there were fruit orchards between Burwell and Wicken owned by Robert Stevenson of the Manor House, Burwell, who also had land in Exning nearby. His apples were kept in cold storage in a building in the fen that still remains, and this is the interior in 1923 The figures at the right, from the front, are: Frances Faircliffe, Edith Goodchild and Vera Bysouth, and on the left: Mrs Surridge, Arthur Warren, Mrs Gathercole and Hamish Faircliffe. There were apple trees in almost every garden hereabouts at this time, bearing apples of infinite variety, so many of them now beyond recall.

(Cambridgeshire Collection; Dorothy Grainger)

THE APPLE SHOW

Just as keen gardeners like to compete in the annual horticultural shows, the apple growers liked to boost their pride — and trade — by contributing to the apple shows in the Wisbech Corn Exchange, all neatly arranged here in 1956 in a hall permeated with the perfume of juice. The growers remain at the mercy of the weather, but shortages for one generally meant shortages for the other. Pest control techniques were used long ago, the trees being sprayed with lime wash from the ground using a gun in those Burwell orchards in the previous picture in the 1920s. The advertisers sponsored this show and made the best of it, but there is not much room left for pride among the fruitgrowers of the fens.

(Lilian Ream)

THE PICKERS ARRIVE

This is what happened each year to swell the numbers required to pick the fruit from the Wisbech orchards between the wars. They arrived in droves at Wisbech Station from the East End of London, rather like the hoppickers arriving in Kent, treating it as an annual working holiday in the fresh air, bringing their children and babies with them. They went into farm camps keeping crowded company as was their wont, and there were back-up nursing services for the infants and entertainments in the Wisbech Corn Exchange for all. Cambridge undergraduates arrived in motor cars in a spirit of patronage, but genuinely to help out, and the pickers went home healthier and wealthier after bringing some trade to the town.

(Lilian Ream)

THE FARM CAMP

The London fruit pickers were accommodated in such as this Redmoor Camp in Elm, near Wisbech, in 1931, which ensured the communal life to which they were accustomed in the city. They are having their lunches here in Ayres' Bunkhouse, gratifying appetites sharpened by the clean air and climbing exercise, camaraderie shining on their faces. For a while, at least, they must have felt the claustrophobia of their environment when they got home. Friday Bridge International Farm Camp remains off the March road while looking no better than a collection of drab prisoner-of-war huts.

(Lilian Ream)

DAHLIAS

Many fen villagers grow flowers commercially as a sideline, using small fields and large allotments, or even their own gardens if they are big. They pack their flowers in supplied boxes daily in summer, and they are collected by lorry and taken to the cities direct. The flowers they grow for this are long-lasting when cut, but for local markets they might, late in the season, cut such as dahlias which have a short life in the vase. Grown on a wide scale, however, dahlias are there to produce tubers for the garden trade, as in this sunny field near Wisbech in the 1960s, tended by women for the Wisbech Bulb Company.

(Lilian Ream)

TULIPS

Dutchmen made our fens what they are, and the farmers this century have continued to make them look more like Holland by growing flowers in abundance. Once flower-growing was seen to be a commercial proposition, then tulips from Amsterdam became tulips from Spalding, where they mount an internationally famed tulip festival each year to prove it. Wisbech counters with a Rose Fair to celebrate its own choice of flower from the fen nurseries. Hundreds of acres are given over to flowers to supply the towns and cities with blooms each day, and to produce more bulbs for the burgeoning garden-centre trade. The crops needed more hands yesterday than they do today when planting is done by machine, but they are still labour intensive. Here we see tulip picking for Mr Hobson Bateman at Long Sutton in the 1930s. His Seagate Farm with its six-sailed windmill is behind.

(Lilian Ream)

DAFFODILS

Winter is still with us when the daffodils bloom, and the flower-cutting season can go on into November. Tulips, gladioli and daffodils were produced on a hundred acres by J.R. Bateman and Sons of Sutton St Edmund in 1950, and this is their packing station at Sutton Bridge in full production for the daily supplies to Covent Garden. Mr Bateman was the son of Hobson Bateman in the previous picture. The wartime habit of wearing turbans, like the munition workers then, persists here, but the faces are smiling like the flowers. But such a labour force is no longer employed at this farm, for Mr Bateman has gone back to cereal and root crops. The small flower growers complain of low profits, and for the large grower such a workforce does make life complicated. But the plains remain pretty in spring , summer and into autumn, and it is perhaps gratifying to learn that bulbs produced in the fens have been exported to Holland where a bulb disease has caused problems. Fields cannot grow flowers continuously, and crop rotation is necessary.

(Lilian Ream)

HOME

This is home in the fens as I knew it. Briscoe Snelson of Cambridge was a rural poet with a camera, dedicated to recording the tender corners of the fen landscape imbued with the spirit of home and contentment. Such there were aplenty between the wars, like this scene near Fordey Farm some three miles from Ely, where nothing heavier than a horse and a loaded cart has made its mark. Snelson chose the moment of Sunday serenity, that inviolable time of leisure for man and beast, allowing the horses to get used to his presence before taking his picture. We are indebted to him for capturing so many peaceful scenes now gone or badly spoiled, from a time when farming was a way of life, sooner than a hardheaded business carried out while laying the countryside bare. This is England unspoiled by heavy machines and chemicals, by over-efficiency, by ugliness at one extreme and over-tidiness at the other, by the replacement of English trees by leylandii conifers, by the temptations of travel that have taken away the sense of home and beauty in sheltered places such as this.

(Cambridgeshire Collection; Briscoe Snelson)

ACKNOWLEDGEMENTS

For this book I have relied more than ever on the extensive photographic archive of the Cambridgeshire Collection in the Lion Yard, Cambridge, and on the patient service given by Michael Petty, Chris Jakes and their staff. I am also indebted to David Rayner for supplying me with prints from the rich Lilian Ream archive in Wisbech, and to those individual photographers mentioned both for their timely pictures and their memories. I am grateful to many a fen farmer for talking to me over the telephone, and to those studies of *The Cambridgeshire Coprolite Mining Rush* by Richard Grove, *Woad in the Fens* by Norman Wills and *The Fenland Story*, that brilliant summary by W.E. Dring, while, inevitably, I have dipped for information into A.K. Astbury's *The Black Fens* and James Wentworth Day's *A History of the Fens* which have become part of our heritage. My thanks, as always, to Steve Benz of SB Publications for his encouragement and support.

S.B. Publications publish a wide range of local history titles. For a full list write (enclosing S.A.E.) to:-
S.B. Publications, c/o 19 Grove Road, Seaford, East Sussex BN25 1TP.